HERBERT HOWELLS

ELEGY

for viola & piano

or viola, string quartet & string orchestra

Piano reduction by
John Glenesk Mortimer

BOOSEY & HAWKES

Boosey & Hawkes Music Publishers Ltd
www.boosey.com

COMPOSER'S NOTE

This work was composed in 1917, and first performed at the Mons Memorial Concert at the Royal Albert Hall in the same year, by Sir Hugh Allen and the London Symphony Orchestra. It is inscribed to the memory of Francis Purcell Warren, a fellow-student of the composer at the Royal College of Music in the years of the First World War. He was a Viola Scholar, and composer; and also one of the circle of young musicians that included Gurney, Eugene Goossens, Arthur Benjamin, Arthur Bliss and the present writer himself – all fellow-students at one time. Purcell Warren was killed in the 1914–1918 War, and this *Elegy* was composed soon after his death. It is not in the least 'heroic': it was entirely dominated (in my mind) by the personality of my friend.

HH

ANMERKUNG DES KOMPONISTEN

Dieses Werk wurde 1917 komponiert und erstmalig im selben Jahr beim Mons Memorial Konzert in der Royal Albert Hall von Sir Hugh Allen und dem London Symphony Orchestra aufgeführt. Es steht in Erinnerung an Francis Purcell Warren, einem Kommilitonen des Komponisten am Royal College of Music in den Jahren des Ersten Weltkrieges. Er war Viola-Schüler und Komponist; außerdem gehörte er dem Kreis junger Musiker an, zu dem Gurney, Eugene Goossens, Arthur Benjamin, Arthur Bliss und der Autor selber zählten – sie alle studierten zu einem Zeitpunkt zusammen. Purcell Warren wurde im Krieg 1914–1918 getötet, und diese *Elegie* wurde kurz nach seinem Tod komponiert. Sie ist in keinster Weise „heroisch": in meinem Geist wurde sie vollkommen von der Persönlichkeit meines Freundes beherrscht.

HH (Übersetzung: Heike Römer)

NOTE DU COMPOSITEUR

Cette œuvre a été composée en 1917, et jouée pour la première fois au Mons Memorial Concert au Royal Albert Hall la même année, par Sir Hugh Allen et le London Symphony Orchestra. Elle est dédiée à la mémoire de Francis Purcell Warren, un condisciple du compositeur au Royal College of Music pendant les années de la Première Guerre mondiale. Il était Viola Scholar, et compositeur; et aussi l'un des membres du cercle de jeunes musiciens qui incluaient Gurney, Eugene Goosens, Arthur Benjamin, Arthur Bliss, et le présent auteur lui-même – tous condisciples à une époque. Purcell Warren a été tué pendant la Guerre de 1914–1918, et cette *Élégie* a été composée peu après sa mort. Elle n'est pas du tout «héroïque»: elle était entièrement dominée (dans mon esprit) par la personnalité de mon ami.

HH (Traduction: Francis Marchal)

Duration: 10 minutes

Orchestral performance materials available on hire

Recommended recording: Chandos CHAN 9161,
by the City of London Sinfonia, conducted by Richard Hickox

Published by Boosey & Hawkes Music Publishers Ltd
Aldwych House
71–91 Aldwych
London
WC2B 4HN

www.boosey.com

ISMN 979-0-060-13029-8
ISBN 978-1-78454-113-2

First impression 2015. Third impression 2016

Printed by Halstan:
Halstan UK, 2–10 Plantation Road, Amersham, Bucks, HP6 6HJ. United Kingdom
Halstan DE, Weißliliengasse 4, 55116 Mainz. Germany

Cover photo: Herbert Howells © The Herbert Howells Society
Music origination by Topscore Music

To the memory of Francis Purcell Warren

ELEGY

for viola, string quartet
& string orchestra

Piano reduction by
JOHN GLENESK MORTIMER

HERBERT HOWELLS
(1892–1983)

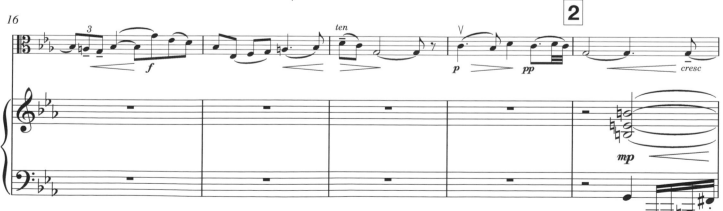

03163

Published by Boosey & Hawkes Music Publishers Ltd
Aldwych House
71–91 Aldwych
London
WC2B 4HN

www.boosey.com

© Copyright 1938 by Hawkes & Son (London) Ltd
This arrangement © copyright 2015 by Hawkes & Son (London) Ltd

ISMN 979-0-060-13029-8
ISBN 978-1-78454-113-2

First impression 2015. Third impression 2016

Printed by Halstan:
Halstan UK, 2–10 Plantation Road, Amersham, Bucks, HP6 6HJ. United Kingdom
Halstan DE, Weißliliengasse 4, 55116 Mainz. Germany

Cover photo: Herbert Howells © The Herbert Howells Society
Music origination by Topscore Music

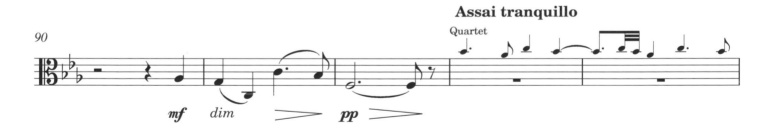

To the memory of Francis Purcell Warren

Solo Viola

ELEGY
for viola, string quartet
& string orchestra

Piano reduction by
JOHN GLENESK MORTIMER

HERBERT HOWELLS
(1892–1983)

Quasi lento, teneramente

03163

67

71

estinto - - - - - -

con sord

8 **Assai tranquillo (tempo I)**

75

80

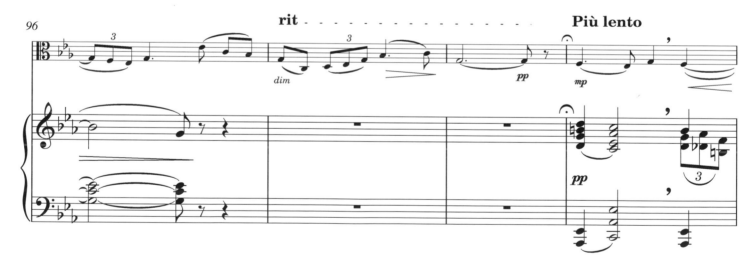

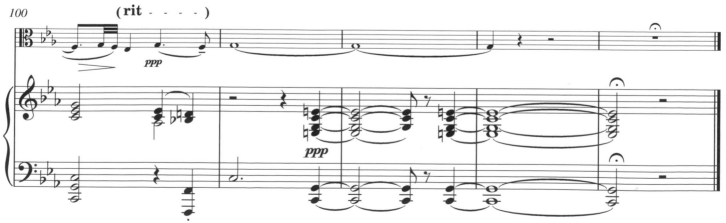